D0896720

COMMON TREE DISEASES
OF BRITISH COLUMBIA
(Second Edition)

by
R. E. Foster
and
G. W. Wallis

Department of the Environment
Canadian Forestry Service
Publication No. 1245
Ottawa, 1974

Published under the authority of the
Minister of Fisheries and Forestry
Ottawa, 1969

First edition, 1969 _____ 7,300
Second edition, 1974 _____ 6,000

Information Canada
Ottawa, 1974
Catalogue No. Fo 47-1245
Contract No. KL020-4-P015
Maracle Press

PREFACE

An earlier publication "Some common tree diseases of British Columbia" by the late J. E. Bier was issued by the Canada Department of Agriculture in 1949. It dealt with most of the forest diseases then recognized as important or potentially damaging in British Columbia. Since then, other diseases have been studied and are considered to be damaging; they are included in this publication. However, not every disease known to occur in the province is described; some are omitted because of restricted distribution or minor importance and others pending more comprehensive surveys and information on their distribution and economic significance.

Anyone finding a disease associated with forest losses is requested to submit a sample, with a report, to the Pacific Forest Research Centre, 506 West Burnside Road, Victoria, B.C., V8Z 1M5. Reports of this nature are a valuable adjunct to the regular survey of forest diseases carried out by the Laboratory.

In this second edition the scientific names of six diseases have been changed, and nine 'new' ones have been included in the index and text. *Rhabdocline pseudotsugae* has been divided into two species. A few changes have been made in the general descriptions and in three captions.

CONTENTS

INTRODUCTION

A forest tree disease may be defined as an injurious condition, often expressed by the abnormal growth or development of a tree, caused by an agent other than fire or insects. This definition includes disorders that culminate in tree death and those that reduce growth, lower quality, or cause predisposition to attack by other agents.

A diseased tree may be detected from symptoms or signs. **Symptoms**[1] are expressed by the abnormal growth or development of the tree; for example, the appearance of dead or dying plant parts. **Signs** are evidence of the causal agent of disease; for example, a **conk** or other type of external growth of a **fungus.**

Non-infectious or physiological diseases are caused by non-living agents which do not spread from one tree to another but simultaneously affect trees growing within the same environment. They encompass a wide range of disturbances to the normal functioning of a tree; e.g., those caused by unfavorable climate, a deficiency or excess of nutrients or moisture, or atmospheric pollution. Different tree species and trees of different ages and vigor vary in their susceptibility to damage. Factors inducing physiological disorders may operate for only a brief period as in the case of frost, or may extend over part of the growing season as in the case of a prolonged summer drought, or their effects may be cumulative over a period of years as in the case of atmospheric pollution.

Infectious diseases are caused by living agents, such as fungi, bacteria and higher plants that attack trees to obtain food materials essential to their development. The severity of loss depends on the relative susceptibility of the tree, the **virulence** and life history of the causal agent, and the environmental and other circumstances that influence the resistance of the **host** and the growth and reproductive ability of the causal agent. Consequently, a disease may vary in importance between tree species in one region or in the same tree species in adjacent regions.

Infectious forest diseases are classed as native or introduced. Native diseases do not usually threaten the existence of a tree species, but they may cause severe losses in stands that are maintained beyond maturity, or are otherwise of poor vigor, or if weather and other environmental conditions have been abnormal. Introduced (extra-regional or foreign) diseases, such as white pine blister rust, may become **epidemic** and threaten the existence of a susceptible tree species throughout its entire range. The danger

---

[1] Words in bold face are defined in the Glossary.

always exists that other diseases, equally as damaging as white pine blister rust, may become established in other commercial tree species.

Most of the infectious diseases that occur in British Columbia are caused by fungi. Microscopic examination is required to identify many of the causal agents but most of those included in this handbook may be recognized by their gross appearance (signs) or by associated symptoms.

NON-INFECTIOUS DISEASES

Cedar flagging

Although not a disease, reference is made to cedar **flagging** because of interest in its cause and significance. Flagging is a normal condition in western red cedar; entire branchlets die during dry, hot summers or toward the end of the growing season. It is recognized by the occurrence of isolated branchlets bearing yellow or red, dying or dead foliage (Fig. 1). The condition is not believed to have a detrimental effect on tree growth.

Pole blight

Pole blight has been confined to pole-sized western white pine. The first evidence of its presence is a reduction of leader and branch growth (Fig. 2), internodal lengths commonly being only a fraction of the length of internodes on adjacent unaffected trees. Old needles drop prematurely and the remaining needles, clustered toward the end of the twigs, are short and yellow and few in number. **Symptoms** progress downward and inward, the entire crown eventually becoming relatively open (Fig. 3). Trees affected by pole blight can usually be distinguished from trees infected by blister rust; in the former the entire crown is affected whereas in the latter only that portion of the crown above the blister rust **canker** exhibits disease symptoms (Fig. 45). A distinctive symptom of pole blight affected trees is the presence of flat or depressed areas in the bark of stems (Fig. 4) that may cover long, narrow **lesions** in the sapwood (Fig. 5). Lesions can often be detected by the presence of an excessive flow of resin (Fig. 4). The occurrence of **callusing** at the margin of lesions is indicative that trees are recovering from the disease.

Pole blight is believed to be induced by extended periods of unusually warm and dry weather. Dry sites and low soil fertility are thought to be conducive to the occurrence of the disease.

Fig. 1. Flagging in western red cedar.

Fig. 2. Reduced leader and branch growth characteristic of pole blight affected western white pine.

Fig. 3. Pole blight affected western white pine. Note the relatively open crown with the needles tufted at the ends of the branches.

4

Fig. 4. Depressed area in the bark and excessive resin flow on the stem of a western white pine tree affected with pole blight.

Fig. 5. Long, narrow lesion in the sapwood below the depressed area in the bark noted in Fig. 4.

Terminal injury

Terminal injury is manifested by a broken top or by the aborted development of terminal buds resulting in a double or multiple leader (Fig. 6). In young trees, broken tops have been attributed to snow and ice and to injuries caused by animals, birds and insects; in older trees broken tops may result from the action of snow or wind. The various causes of terminal bud injury are not known, but severe frosts and insects are believed to be partly responsible. Multiple leader formation is not necessarily of consequence; unless a tree is affected repeatedly, one of the leaders will assume dominance and the reduction in height growth will be negligible.

Frost lesions

Frost **lesions** can result from a sudden drop in air temperature before plant tissues have hardened-off. The bark and **cambium** are killed, forming a localized lesion. Eventually, the dead tissues covering the lesions are sloughed-off, exposing the sapwood. Several years may be required before the lesion is **callused**-over (Fig. 7); during this period the exposed wood is susceptible to attack by **fungi** capable of extensive development within both the sapwood and underlying heartwood (Fig. 8). All tree species are believed to be susceptible to damage.

Sunscald

Sunscald is a condition caused by the intense heat of direct sun rays. Damaged areas of the main stem, generally on the southwest side of trees, are initially copper to bright red and stand out in marked contrast to healthy bark (Fig. 9). These bright colors are not persistent and it may be difficult after a period of time to recognize previously damaged tissues. In severe cases, the bark in the affected area may become scaly and slough off. Rapidly growing trees, trees suffering from drought, and those suddenly exposed to strong sunlight, as may occur following thinning or pruning, appear to be the most susceptible. Apparently there is no permanent injury unless the affected portions are killed when open scars are formed through which wood-decaying **fungi** may gain entrance to susceptible tissues.

Fig. 6. Apical bud injury in Douglas-fir showing double leaders produced from lateral apical buds.

7

Fig. 7. Callused frost lesion on Douglas-fir.

Fig. 8. Old frost lesion in Douglas-fir showing complete callusing, partial frost ring, and red stain associated with *Haematostereum (Stereum) sanguinolentum.*

8

9

Fig. 9. Sunscald in Douglas-fir showing range in bark coloration from healthy lower section to severely affected central section, to moderately affected upper section.

9

Top killing

Top killing of trees may be caused by **fungi**, insects or climatic disturbances such as low temperature, drought or flooding. Killing by low temperature is most likely to occur in exposed areas, such as ridges, or in frost pockets at lower elevations. Drought injury is generally more prevalent on sites of low moisture-holding capacity; shoot **dieback** may be progressive if the moisture deficiency is severe and prolonged, appearing first in the upper crown (Fig. 10) and gradually extending towards the base of the tree. Fungi may attack the weakened or dead portions of the stem, extending the damage to adjacent tissues.

Basal and trunk scars

Basal and trunk scars are caused by a number of agents; consequently, associated **symptoms** may be variable. In general, charring indicates a fire origin, extensive scars accompanied by broken or missing branches suggest damage caused by falling trees, and scars encompassing branches indicate animal or **fungus** attack (Fig. 11). Logging activities frequently cause tree scars, usually of irregular outline and sometimes deeply gouged (Fig. 12). Various diseases, notably armillaria root rot, are responsible for basal **lesions**.

A direct loss in volume may result from scarring and an additional indirect loss can be expected if the scarred areas are infected by stain- or decay-producing fungi; the former reduce the quality and the latter destroy the merchantable wood (Fig. 13).

Fig. 10. Terminal leader dieback in western hemlock.

Fig. 11. Old bear scar on western white pine. Note the intact branches and shreds of bark at the apex.

Fig. 12. Deeply gouged basal scar on spruce caused by a bulldozer.

Fig. 13. Decay in western white pine associated with an old basal scar.

Sapsucker damage

Sapsuckers are one of several groups of birds that cause tree damage; specific reference is made to sapsuckers because they attack only living trees and have caused damage to many tree species in British Columbia. Their feeding habits produce punctures through the bark that are in definite patterns, e.g., partial rings around tree limbs or uniform vertical rows on the main stem (Fig. 14). These punctures can serve as entry points for stain- and decay-producing **fungi** that cause permanent damage to the tree.

Winter kill

Although very low temperatures may be required to kill trees, particularly if they are established on good sites, temperatures just below freezing are sufficient to cause damage to foliage which has not hardened-off. Foliage may be killed if exposed to warm drying winds when the ground is frozen because the trees are unable to replace the water lost through transpiration; the needles become dessicated, turn red and die (Fig. 15). In mountainous regions injury may be confined to an altitudinal zone corresponding to the pathway of drying winds, hence the common name "red belt". Height and diameter growth are retarded and damaged trees are weakened and predisposed to attack by other agents.

Fume injury

Trees are susceptible to injury from noxious industrial fumes. The foliage usually absorbs the toxic gases for a prolonged period before the injury becomes visible. **Symptoms** and severity of damage vary between tree species, between concentration and type of gas, duration of exposure, and distance from the source of the fumes. Generally, discoloration of conifer needles starts at the tips (Fig. 16), while broadleaved foliage is affected first in the tissues between the veins, giving the leaf a mottled appearance (Fig. 17). Foliage, buds, branches and entire trees may be killed; the damage sometimes occurs over an extensive area.

Fig. 14. Vertical rows of "sap-wells" caused by red-breasted sapsucker feeding on amabilis fir.

15

Fig. 15. Winter kill on Douglas-fir.

Fig. 16. Fume damage to Douglas-fir.

Fig. 17. Fume damage to broadleaf maple.

INFECTIOUS DISEASES

Root and Butt Rots

Armillaria mellea (Fr.) Kumm.

causing armillaria root rot

Armillaria mellea is widely distributed throughout the forest regions of the world, attacking most coniferous and deciduous tree species as well as a wide range of other plants. Its importance has not been fully appraised in British Columbia, but it is recognized as the cause of root rot in young Douglas-fir and of butt rot in mature trees, particularly western hemlock, western red cedar and the true firs.

Infected trees occur singly or in groups. In plantations, infected trees are frequently found in close proximity to stumps of the previous stand; roots of the young trees are probably infected when they come in contact with the **fungus** in the infected stumps or roots. There is evidence that damage may vary considerably between different tree species and regions; very severe attacks are usually localized. Trees under stress are highly susceptible, but healthy, vigorous trees are also attacked without apparent predisposition. Some trees, even though in an advanced state of decline, may recover.

The first evidence of attack is a progressive decline in height growth; leader growth in young trees is moderately to severely reduced for 2 to 5 years prior to death (Fig. 18). **Chlorotic** foliage and a heavy flow of pitch at the base of the trunk (Fig. 19), and a distress crop of cones usually become evident during the period of growth decline. Some of these **symptoms** are also associated with other root disorders, but attack by *A. mellea* can be verified by the presence of a fan-like growth of **mycelium** under the bark at the base of the tree (Fig. 21), or by the presence of dark brown to black shoestring-like structures **(rhizomorphs)** on or under the bark (Fig. 22). The fungus spreads from tree to tree by means of root contacts or rhizomorphs.

The **fruiting bodies** are mushrooms which usually develop in clusters (Fig. 20) at the base of an infected tree, generally in the late summer and fall. They have a honey-colored cap with dark scales and white gills, a yellow-brown or rusty-tinged stem, and an inconspicuous ring surrounding the upper part of the stem.

18

18

Fig. 18. Douglas-fir infected with *Armillaria mellea* showing thin foliage, reduced terminal growth and a distress cone crop.

19

Fig. 19. Basal resinosis associated with *Armillaria mellea* infection.

Fig. 20. Sporophores (mushrooms) of *Armillaria mellea* growing from the root collar of an infected Douglas-fir tree.

20

Fig. 21. Mycelial fans below the bark at the base of the stem of a Douglas-fir tree infected with *Armillaria mellea*.

Fig. 22. Rhizomorphs of *Armillaria mellea*.

21

Poria weirii Murr.

causing poria root rot

Poria weirii is widely distributed throughout British Columbia and the Pacific Northwest and it attacks most coniferous tree species; hardwoods appear to be immune. Poria root rot is regarded as the most important disease affecting immature forests of Douglas-fir. It also occurs as a butt rot in mature conifers, particularly western red cedar.

Infected trees occur in groups which enlarge from a focal center (Fig. 23). Crown **symptoms** are not usually evident until the **fungus** is well established in the roots. Eventually, there is retardation of height growth and thinning and yellowing of the foliage; a crop of distress cones may be formed (Fig. 18). White to mauve-colored **mycelium** can usually be found on the bark at the root collar and on roots. **Resinosis** is rare. Trees with advanced root deterioration are frequently windthrown, producing typical "root-balls" (Fig. 23).

The early stage of decay appears as a red-brown stain in the outer heartwood (Fig. 24). Infection rarely extends more than 6 to 10 feet up the bole in living trees. Later, the stained wood becomes soft, small pits appear, and the annual rings separate to form a typical **laminate** decay (Fig. 25). Accumulations of brown mycelium can be found between the sheets of decayed wood, forming a diagnostic feature of this rot.

The fungus remains viable in stumps and other woody material for many years,[1] providing the major source of **inoculum** for a subsequent generation of trees. **Spores** are not believed to be important in disseminating the disease and the mycelium does not grow freely in the soil. Following the initial infection of a root from an infected stump, the mycelium spreads along the bark surface as well as in the wood. Infection of adjacent healthy trees occurs when their roots come in contact with diseased roots.

Sporophores appear as brown, crust-like layers on upturned roots and on the undersides of decayed logs (Fig. 26). When fresh, they are light buff with a white margin; later they turn a uniform dark brown. The exposed surface of the sporophore is **poroid** and the pores are small and regular in outline.

Fig. 23. *Poria weirii* infection center in a 50-year-old stand of Douglas-fir.

Fig. 24. Red-brown incipient decay in the butt of a Douglas-fir tree caused by *Poria weirii*.

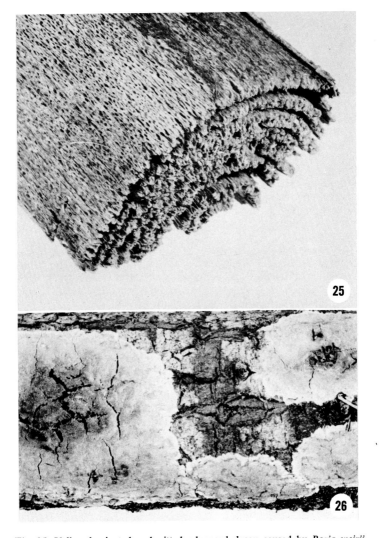

Fig. 25. Yellow laminated and pitted advanced decay caused by *Poria weirii*.

Fig. 26. Brown sporophores of *Poria weirii* growing flat on the underside of a decayed Douglas-fir log.

25

Fomes annosus (Fr.) Karst.

causing annosus root rot

Fomes annosus is known throughout the temperate zone as the cause of butt rot of mature coniferous trees, and of butt and root rot that seriously affects the growth and survival of plantations and young forests. The **fungus** has a very wide host range including both coniferous and broadleaved species; western hemlock appears to be the most highly susceptible of the native coniferous species.

The fungus gains entry to individual trees and forests through **spore** infection of injuries and exposed surfaces of freshly cut stumps; spores are carried by air currents for many miles. It is able to develop and survive in stumps for many years. Local spread occurs at points of contact between healthy and diseased roots, therefore, infected trees tend to occur in groups. Pines are frequently killed by *Fomes* while infection in other tree species usually results in butt rot.

The **incipient** stage of decay appears as a yellow-brown to red-brown stain (Fig. 27). Later, the wood is reduced to a white stringy or spongy mass (Fig. 28) containing numerous small black flecks running parallel to the grain. In the final stage the wood is completely destroyed, leaving a hollow butt.

Sporophores are perennial, woody to leathery, and vary in form from **effused-reflexed** to bracket-like. The upper surface (Fig. 29) is zoned, dark brown to black, and has an **acute** margin. The lower surface (Fig. 30) is white to cream, and **poroid**; the pores are small and regular in outline. The **context** is white or cream. Sporophores rarely form on living trees except on dead roots or in association with basal scars; they are produced more frequently on upturned roots, old stumps or slash.

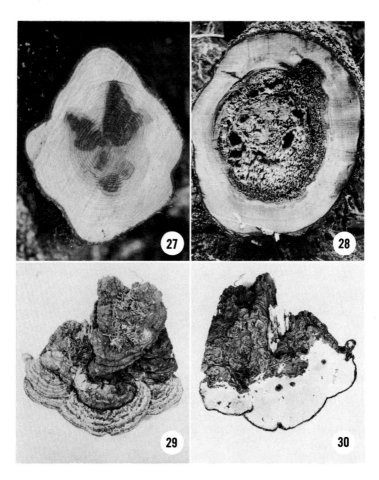

Fig. 27. Yellow-brown incipient decay in western hemlock caused by *Fomes annosus*.

Fig. 28. White stringy to spongy advanced decay in western hemlock caused by *Fomes annosus*.

Fig. 29. Upper surface of the sporophore of *Fomes annosus*.

Fig. 30. Lower surface of the sporophore of *Fomes annosus*.

27

Polyporus schweinitzii Fr.

causing brown cubical butt rot

Polyporus schweinitzii, the velvet top **fungus,** is the cause of a butt rot of many species of mature trees but it also attacks younger trees. In British Columbia losses are most severe in mature Douglas-fir and Sitka spruce. Decay generally occurs in the high quality basal log. Trees with rot are subject to wind breakage and a small volume of decay may cause the total loss of a tree.

Polyporus schweinitzii enters trees through basal wounds such as fire scars and probably spreads by root contact.

The **incipient** stage of decay appears as a light yellow stain. Later the wood becomes brittle and breaks into large reddish brown cubes (Fig. 32). A characteristic odor, similar to oil of anise, is often associated with advanced decay.

The **sporophores** are annual, generally forming in late summer, spongy to leathery, and shelving (Fig. 31) or **stipitate** (Fig. 33). The upper surface often shows concentric rings and is reddish brown and velvety, hence the common name "the velvet top fungus". The margin is rounded, and is light yellow-green in contrast to other dark areas of the upper surface. The lower surface is yellow-green (turning brown when bruised) and **poroid**; the pores are relatively large and often irregular in outline. The **context** is yellow-green to light brown. In old specimens the entire sporophore becomes reddish brown.

Sporophores rarely form on living trees; they develop on felled timber (Fig. 31) and on the forest floor near the base of an infected tree. Sporophores in the latter position indicate root infection but not necessarily extensive development of butt rot.

Fig. 31. Shelf-like sporophores of *Polyporus schweinitzii*.

Fig. 32. Advanced decay caused by *Polyporus schweinitzii* illustrating the breakdown of the wood into large red-brown cubes.

Fig. 33. Stipitate sporophore of *Polyporus schweinitzii* showing large, irregular pores on lower surface.

Dwarf Mistletoes

Arceuthobium spp.

The dwarf mistletoes are **parasitic** flowering plants, capable of survival only on living conifers. Although a specific mistletoe may attack more than one **host** species, usually only one species is severely damaged. Western red cedar, yellow cedar, western yew and juniper appear to be immune from infection but all other native coniferous species in British Columbia are susceptible to attack by mistletoe species.

Dwarf mistletoe infection is generally recognized by swellings on the main stem (Fig. 34) or branches (Fig. 38), by witches' brooms (Fig. 35) or by the presence of the aerial shoots. Heavy infections cause reduction in height and diameter growth and in wood quality, and sometimes result in the death of the tree. Dead tissues, resulting from the parasitic action of the mistletoe plant, provide entrance points for stain- and decay-producing **fungi.**

The dwarf mistletoes produce male (Fig. 36) and female plants (Figs. 37, 38). Following fertilization, the female plant produces green to dark brown berries (Fig. 38) from which the mature seeds are forcibly ejected for distances up to 40 feet. The seed, covered with a sticky, mucilaginous pulp, must germinate on and penetrate the bark of a susceptible host to survive. After penetration, a system of strands and perennial sinkers develops in the inner bark. The sinkers ultimately come in contact with and become imbedded in the woody tissues of the tree causing distortion of the annual rings and swelling of bark and wood tissues (Fig. 39). Aerial shoots, buds and flowers usually develop within 3 years of initial infection. The shoots of the Douglas-fir mistletoe are only about 1 inch long (Fig. 37), whereas those of other mistletoes, such as the lodgepole pine mistletoe (Fig. 36), may be 5 inches long.

The aerial growth of the mistletoe plant is sometimes attacked by insects and fungi; one of the most common of the fungal parasites produces clusters of small black **fruiting bodies** at the tips of the female flowers, inhibiting the development of the mistletoe fruit and seed (Fig. 40).

Commonly occurring dwarf mistletoes and their major hosts in British Columbia include:

Arceuthobium americanum Nutt. ex Engelm. on lodgepole pine in the Interior (Figs. 35, 36).

Arceuthobium douglasii Engelm. on Douglas-fir in the Interior (Fig. 37).

Arceuthobium laricis (Piper) St. John on western larch.

Arceuthobium tsugense (Rosendahl) G. N. Jones on western hemlock and lodgepole pine on the Coast (Fig. 34).

Fig. 34. Swelling on the main stem of western hemlock caused by dwarf mistletoe.

31

Fig. 35. Witches' broom on lodgepole pine caused by dwarf mistletoe.

Fig. 36. Male dwarf mistletoe plant growing on lodgepole pine.
Fig. 37. Female dwarf mistletoe plants growing on Douglas-fir.

38

Fig. 38. Female dwarf mistletoe plant with mature berries, and swelling on lodgepole pine branch caused by the infection.

Fig. 39. Five-year-old dwarf mistletoe infection of western hemlock illustrating distortion of the annual rings and swelling of bark and woody tissues.

Fig. 40. Small black fruit bodies of the secondary parasite *Wallrothiella arceuthobii* infecting the immature fruit of a dwarf mistletoe plant.

35

Stem and Branch Diseases — Rusts

The tree rusts comprise a large and complex group of the forest **fungi.** They are **obligate parasites,** requiring living **hosts** for survival; with few exceptions, tree rusts require a primary and an alternate host plant to complete their life cycle. They are host-specific or are capable of attacking only a narrow range of plants. They produce as many as five different **spore** states.

Stem rusts gain entrance to the primary host trees through needles; the **hyphae** grow into the needle-bearing branch and eventually into the main stem. Stems and branches may be girdled by the fungus resulting in the death of the branch or stem above the point of girdling; the infection may also cause malformations such as galls (Fig. 41), witches' brooms (Fig. 42) or resin-soaked **cankers** (Fig. 43). Blisters containing yellow spore masses (Fig. 44) break through the bark within the zone of infection and release spores that infect the alternate host. Subsequently, other spores are produced on the alternate host that are capable of re-infecting only that host species, thus intensifying the disease. Later, still other spores are produced on these alternate hosts that can infect only the primary host, thus completing the life cycle.

Some common stem and branch rusts affecting British Columbia tree species are:

Western gall rust, *Endocronartium harknessii* (J. P. Moore) Y. Hiratsuka (Fig. 41): evidence suggests that this is a non-alternating rust apparently confined to 2- and 3-needle pines.

Fir broom rust, *Melampsorella caryophyllacearum* Schroet. (Fig. 42): alternating between the true firs and chickweed.

Spruce broom rust, *Chrysomyxa arctostaphyli* Diet.: alternating between spruce and bearberry (*Arctostaphylos uva-ursi* (L.) Spreng.).

Stalactiform rust, *Cronartium coleosporioides* Arth. (Fig. 44): alternating between lodgepole pine and several herbaceous plants, including Indian paint brush (*Castilleja miniata* Dougl. ex Hook.).

Comandra blister rust, *Cronartium comandrae* Peck: alternating between 2- and 3-needle pines and toad flax (*Comandra* spp.).

Sweetfern blister rust, *Cronartium comptoniae* Arth.: alternating between 2- and 3-needle pines and sweet gale (*Myrica gale* L.).

White pine blister rust, *Cronartium ribicola* J. C. Fisch. ex Rab. (Figs. 45-47): alternating between 5-needle pines and *Ribes* spp. (currants and gooseberries).

Fig. 41. Gall on the main stem of lodgepole pine caused by infection by western gall rust.

Fig. 42. Witches' broom on alpine fir caused by *Melampsorella* rust infection.

Fig. 43. Resin-soaked canker on the stem of lodgepole pine caused by rust infection.

Fig. 44. Blisters on the stem of lodgepole pine containing yellow spore masses of the stalactiform rust.

Cronartium ribicola J. C. Fisch. ex Rab.

causing white pine blister rust

White pine blister rust is the most important disease affecting 5-needle pines in North America. It is believed to have been introduced to British Columbia in 1910, but was not discovered until 1921. Five-needle pines are affected throughout their range in North America and losses are severe.

The disease is particularly serious in seedlings; very few escape infection and most are killed within a few years. In older trees, infection is often confined to isolated branches or the upper crown (Fig. 45) so that only part of the tree is killed.

The volume of white pine is rapidly decreasing in many stands where it was once common or even dominant. It is evident that white pine will not remain a tree of commercial importance unless the rust is controlled.

White pine blister rust alternates between 5-needle pines and its alternate **hosts,** currants and gooseberries (*Ribes* spp.). Infection takes place through pine needles in the fall. Although woody tissues are invaded the following spring, at least 3 years are required for the **fungus** to produce **spores**. In the spring of the third or fourth year yellow blisters (Fig. 46) break through the bark of the branch or stem and **cankers** develop in these areas. The blisters contain the spring spores which are capable of infecting only *Ribes.* Approximately 10 days after infection of the *Ribes,* spore development starts on the leaves and continues throughout the summer (Fig. 47). These summer spores reinfect *Ribes,* thus intensifying the disease on this host. In the fall, other spores are produced on *Ribes* that carry the disease back to pine thereby completing the life cycle.

Fig. 45. Blister rust infection in the stem of western white pine causing the crown above the affected area to die.

Fig. 46. Blisters on the stem of western white pine containing orange-yellow spore masses of white pine blister rust.

47

Fig. 47. Minute orange-yellow pustules on the under side of a *Ribes* leaf indicative of infection by blister rust.

Stem and Branch Diseases — Cankers

Some **fungi** invade stems and branches, producing relatively localized areas of infection in the bark and underlying woody tissues referred to as **cankers** (Fig. 48). Cankers on the main stem below the crown may cause the death of the tree by girdling; those on branches may cause **flagging.**

Cankers may be annual or perennial. In the former, the fungus is active only one season, following which it dies; the canker is then covered by **callus** tissue and a new infection is required to intensify the damage. In perennial cankers, the fungus persists in the affected parts for several years; if its development coincides with the period of tree growth no callus tissue will form; if it is active during the dormant season of the host, successive layers of callus will be formed and a typical target-like canker will develop (Fig. 49). **Fruiting bodies** are generally present for only a brief period; they vary in size, shape and color but are usually small, pinhead-sized structures that erupt through the bark in the cankered area.

Although some canker diseases result in severe damage, most of those found in British Columbia cause only minor losses, usually associated with damage to branches in the lower crown. Most of the causal fungi are weak **parasites,** primarily attacking trees weakened by environmental or other influences.

Common canker diseases in British Columbia include the following:

Diaporthe (Phomopsis) lokoyae Funk on Douglas-fir; annual canker, sometimes causing terminal **dieback** (Fig. 48).

Atropellis piniphila (Weir) Lohm. & Cash on lodgepole pine; perennial canker causing a distortion in growth and a blue-black stain of the sapwood and heartwood (Figs. 50, 51). Damage may be severe in dense stands, particularly those growing on dry sites.

Valsa sordida Nits. on poplar.

Botryosphaeria piceae Funk on spruce; causes perennial, swollen black cankers on living branches.

Discocainia treleasei (Sacc.) J. Reid & Funk on Sitka spruce and western hemlock; causes **fusiform,** swollen cankers.

Potebniamyces balsamicola Smerlis on *Abies* spp.

Nectria coccinea (Pers. ex Fr.) Fr. on maple.

Sclerophoma ambigua Funk & Parker: causes branch dieback and perennial stem cankers on mature dogwood.

Hendersonula toruloidea Nattrass: causes perennial cankers which result in grotesque swellings on the stem of arbutus.

44

Fig. 48. Phomopsis cankers forming around small branches on a Douglas-fir sapling.

Fig. 49. A typical target-like perennial canker.

46

Fig. 50. Atropellis canker on lodgepole pine.

Fig. 51. Atropellis canker on lodgepole pine sectioned to illustrate blue-black stain in the sapwood and heartwood.

47

Stem Diseases — Heart Rots

Decay is caused by the action of wood-destroying **fungi** which penetrate the cell walls of wood and dissolve or modify various wood constituents. These fungi are the major cause of wood destruction in mature forests in British Columbia; losses sustained probably exceed those from all other diseases combined. Some tree species are more subject to decay losses than others; in general, Douglas-fir is less affected than western hemlock, western red cedar or the true firs, but significant differences in the average volume of decay may be encountered between different stands of the same species. These differences can be related to differences in tree age, forest site, stand history and regional variation in the incidence of the different fungi responsible for decay.

The wood-destroying fungi typically gain entrance to living trees through wounds and broken branches and tops. **Spores** which germinate at these sites develop a microscopic **mycelial** growth that ramifies throughout the woody tissues. During this stage, which may continue for many years, the fungus develops within the tree and there may be no outward **sign** of defect. Subsequently, the mycelium aggregates and develops into the reproductive stage (**sporophore, conk, fruit body**) on the exterior of the tree, and produces wind-disseminated spores capable of spreading the fungus to other trees.

Some wood-destroying fungi have a wide **host** range, including both deciduous and coniferous trees, but most are restricted to relatively few species. No native tree species are immune from decay.

Different species of wood-destroying fungi cause different types of decay by altering the physical and chemical properties of wood in various ways. Decays may be classed, on the basis of their appearance at a late stage in the process of decay, as cubical, stringy, **laminate** or pitted. Cubical, or brown rots, develop as the result of extensive destruction of wood cellulose; other types of decay, collectively called white rots, develop as a result of a differential destruction of lignin and cellulose and may be white, yellow or brown. Laboratory tests are usually required to identify the causal agent of a decay in the absence of its associated sporophore.

A number of stages of decay are recognized; e.g. **incipient,** early and advanced. These terms refer to the degree to which the wood has disintegrated; in the incipient stage the predominant feature may be discoloration or stain with or without accompanying loss in strength, the early and advanced stages indicate further physical and chemical deterioration of the wood. All stages are often present concurrently, the incipient stages at the advancing margins of a zone of decay and the more advanced stages near the center.

Decays may be classed as sap rots or heart rots but this classification does not necessarily separate decays caused by different fungi. Most fungi attacking sapwood are also capable of extending their development into the underlying heartwood of a tree, and most of the fungi normally attacking heartwood may also attack sapwood in dead trees.

Another general classification uses the vertical position of decay development within the tree, as, for example, butt, trunk and top rot. These classes are useful in assigning the normal area of attack by a specific fungus but they serve only as a general guide; decay present near the mid-point of the trunk of a tree may in time extend its development into the butt and the top. Similarly, butt and top rots may extend into other portions of the stem. The classification has its basis in the avenues of entrance available to decay-producing fungi; fungi that normally enter through roots and basal scars are more likely to be found in the basal log of a tree, whereas those entering through branch scars would be found in the main part of the trunk, and those entering through broken tops would develop primarily in the upper crown. Other avenues of entrance, however, such as scars from falling trees, may provide an opportunity for a fungus to gain entrance throughout the entire length of the tree. The presence of different **infection courts** and their frequency of occurrence could explain the presence of several decay fungi in the same section of a tree and the different volumes of decay sometimes encountered in adjacent trees of the same species and age.

The absence of a sporophore on a tree does not ensure that it is sound. Some fungi only rarely produce sporophores on living trees, though fruiting may be prolific after the death of the tree.

Haematosterum sanguinolentum (Alb. & Schw. ex Fr.) Pouzar

(*Stereum sanguinolentum* (Alb. & Schw. ex Fr.) Fr.)

causing red heartrot

Haematostereum sanguinolentum, the bleeding **fungus** is a common and important decay-producing fungus of conifers in British Columbia. It is responsible for extensive heart rot in mature pine, northern white and Engelmann spruce and the true firs. In other hosts it is largely a slash-destroyer, although it may occasionally be responsible for heartwood stain and terminal dieback following entry through pruning wounds, logging scars and **lesions** formed as a result of climatic injury. Until recently the fungus was believed to gain entrance to trees chiefly through dead branches; recent evidence, however, has shown that it is a wound pathogen attacking chiefly through freshly exposed wood.

The **incipient** stage of decay is firm and appears as a red-brown heartwood stain (Figs. 8, 52). In the advanced stage, the wood becomes light brown to red-brown and soft and friable in texture. Thin, white **mycelial** fragments may develop in association with advanced decay. Finally, the wood becomes a brown, fibrous, stringy mass.

Sporophores are common on the lower surface of a fallen dead branches and on log ends (Fig. 53) but they are rarely found on dead standing trees. They are annual, leathery and **resupinate** to **effused-reflexed,** often forming thin, crust-like layers. In effused-reflexed forms the upper surface is gray to light brown and zoned. The lower surface is roughened, gray to light brown turning blood-red when bruised, hence the common name the "bleeding fungus". Their small size, resupinate nature, inconspicuous coloration and rare occurrence renders their presence of limited value as indicators of decay in living trees.

Fig. 52. Red-brown stain in the heartwood of western hemlock caused by
Haematostereum (Stereum) sanguinolentum.

Fig. 53. Annual, leathery sporophore of *Haematostereum (Stereum) sanguinolentum* and the red-brown stain in the heartwood.

51

Echinodontium tinctorium (Ell. & Ev.) Ell. & Ev.

causing brown stringy trunk rot

Echinodontium tinctorium, the Indian paint **fungus,** is known to exist only in western North America. It is one of the most destructive wood-destroying fungi in British Columbia. The nature of the decay and pattern of spread of *E. tinctorium* may seriously reduce the value of the affected forest for sawtimber.

Echinodontium tinctorium is distributed throughout coastal and interior forests. Inter-regional differences in its abundance seems to be related to major climatic features which determine the presence of suitable **infection courts.** The fungus gains entry through the stubs of small, suppressed branchlets and variation in their occurrence on living branches resulting from natural pruning are responsible for differences in host susceptibility. Most coniferous tree species are attacked. The true firs are highly susceptible throughout their range, western hemlock is moderately to severely attacked in specific habitats, but Douglas-fir and spruce are seldom attacked.

The early stage of decay appears as a light brown or water-soaked stain in the heartwood. Later the wood darkens to red-brown or yellow-brown. Small rust-colored flecks and occasionally streaks (Fig. 54) and white channels, resembling insect tunnels, may develop. Finally, the wood is reduced to a brown, fibrous, stringy mass (Fig. 55).

Sporophores form on living trees, generally in association with branch stubs (Fig. 56) and when present, form reliable indicators of defect. Substantial volumes of decay are associated with individual sporophores; even when they are confined only to a portion of the bole it can be assumed that most of the heartwood is destroyed.

The upper surface of the perennial, hoof-shaped sporophore is hard, fissured and generally black (Fig. 57). The lower surface bears gray to light brown, downward-directed spines (Figs. 57, 58) on which the **spores** are produced. The **context** of the sporophore is brick-red and the common name "Indian paint fungus" is derived from this.

Fig. 54. Western hemlock infected with *Echinodontium tinctorium* illustrating
the yellow laminated advanced decay with red-brown zone lines.

Fig. 55. Yellow-brown stringy final decay caused by *Echinodontium tinctorium*.

Fig. 56. *Echinodontium tinctorium* sporophores on a living western hemlock tree.

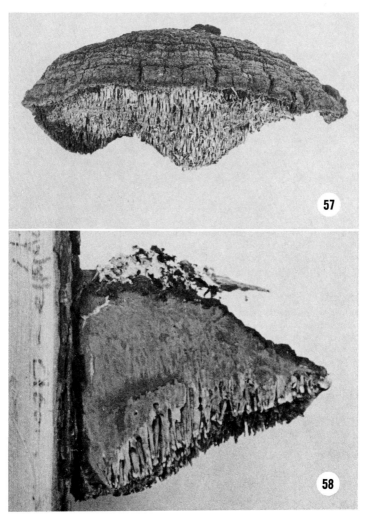

Fig. 57. Perennial hoof-shaped sporophore of *Echinodontium tinctorium* showing fissured upper surface.

Fig. 58. Section through an *Echinodontium tinctorium* sporophore illustrating downward-directed spines on lower surface.

55

Fomes pini (Brot. ex Fr.) Karst.

causing red ring rot

Fomes pini has a wide distribution throughout the north temperate zone and is one of the most common wood-destroying **fungi** in British Columbia. It attacks a wide range of coniferous **hosts** and is particularly damaging in mature Douglas-fir, Sitka and northern white spruce, western hemlock and the true firs. Although the fungus has not been studied in detail in different forest habitats, evidence suggests that greater volumes of wood are damaged on the better sites. In addition to its ability to destroy heartwood, *F. pini* can attack sapwood and cause tree death.

The **incipient** stage of decay appears as a red stain and, in cross sections of logs, often develops as a well defined ring, hence the common name "red ring rot". Later, small, spindle-shaped white pockets (Fig. 59), which run parallel to the grain (Fig. 60), are produced. The latter characteristic of the decay has led to a number of additional common names, e.g. "honeycomb rot" and "white-pitted rot".

Sporophores are produced on living trees (Fig. 61) and may provide a general guide to the amount and distribution of internal decay within one tree species and region. Sporophores often develop adjacent to branch stubs and, in cases of extensive infection, may form more or less along the length of the bole. Punk knots and swollen knots, which are filled with a yellow-brown **mycelial** mass, and constitute early or abortive stages in the development of the sporophore, also indicate the presence of the disease.

The sporophores are hard, woody, perennial and hoof-shaped to bracket-like (Fig. 61), though they may sometimes assume an **effused-reflexed** form when developing on the lower surface of branches. The upper surface is zoned and light to dark brown (Fig. 62). The margin is generally **acute**. The lower surface is light brown and **poroid**; the pores are irregular in outline. The **context** is yellow-brown.

Fig. 59. Advanced red-brown decay with spindle-shaped white pockets in Douglas-fir caused by *Fomes pini*.

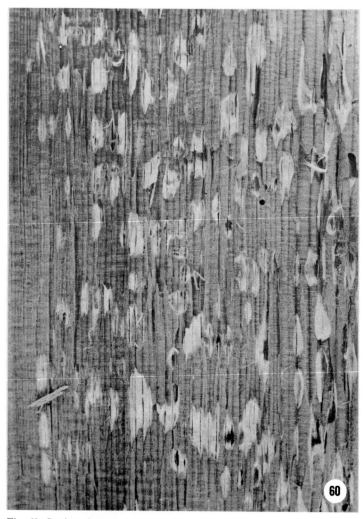

Fig. 60. Section through advanced decay caused by *Fomes pini* illustrating white pockets running parallel to the grain.

Fig. 61. Bracket-like sporophores of *Fomes pini*.

Fig. 62. Zoned upper surface of *Fomes pini* sporophore.

59

Polyporus sulphureus Bull. ex Fr.

causing brown cubical trunk rot

Polyporus sulphureus, the sulphur **fungus**, is responsible for trunk rot in a wide range of coniferous and deciduous **hosts** but is most common in western hemlock (Fig. 63), Sitka spruce and Garry oak.

The **incipient** stage of decay appears as a light brown stain. Later the wood breaks into small brown cubes, sometimes having a rippled appearance, and white, relatively thick **mycelial** felts may form in the shrinkage cracks within the decay (Fig. 64).

The **sporophores** are relatively large, annual, spongy to leathery, bracket-like and occasionally stalked. The upper surface (Fig. 65) is orange-yellow, the **context** white, and the lower surface sulphur-yellow with regular pores. Old specimens become brittle and white throughout. Sporophores seldom form on living coniferous trees but may develop on living hardwoods.

Fig. 63. Large, annual, bracket-like sporophore of *Polyporus sulphureus* on western hemlock.

Fig. 64. Brown cubical decay caused by *Polyporus sulphureus* showing thick white mycelial felts in the cracks.

Fig. 65. Smooth orange-yellow upper surface of a *Polyporus sulphureus* sporophore.

Lentinus kauffmanii A. H. Smith

causing brown pocket rot

Lentinus kauffmanii is responsible for an important butt and trunk decay in Sitka spruce. Although the volume of wood destroyed by this **fungus** is less than that destroyed by others, it is of importance as it frequently occurs in high quality, basal logs and in scattered pockets (Fig. 66), necessitating rejection of logs for lumber production. The amount and pattern of decay visible at log ends seldom provides a reliable indication of the extent of internal defect. Pockets of advanced decay are sharply delimited by apparently sound wood but adjacent pockets may occasionally coalesce to form a continuous column of decay. Within the pockets, the wood breaks into small brown cubes which are soft and friable in texture.

The **sporophore** is a small white mushroom that forms in association with advanced decay in dead trees.

Fig. 66. Brown pocket rot in Sitka spruce caused by *Lentinus kauffmanii*.

Polyporus sericeomollis Rom. (*Poria asiatica* (Pilat) Overh.)

causing cedar pocket rot

Polyporus sericeomollis causes an important butt and trunk rot of western red cedar, ranking second to *Fomes pini* as the most common **fungus** responsible for decay in that species.

The **incipient** decay is straw colored to pale yellow-brown. Later the wood turns light brown, becomes brittle, and breaks down into cubes to form a tubular rot or a series of isolated pockets (Fig. 67).

The **sporophores** are annual, **resupinate**, thin and white, and form on the ends of logs or on slash (Fig. 68).

Poria rivulosa (Berk. & Curt.) Cooke (*Poria albipellucida* Baxt.)

causing white butt rot

Poria rivulosa is the most important butt rot of mature western red cedar in the coast region of British Columbia; because of its development in pole-sized material extensive long-butting is often required.

The early stage of decay appears as a yellow discoloration in the heartwood, sometimes surrounded by a blue to red stain. Radial cracks may form through the decayed wood as it dries. In the late stage of decay, the annual rings separate to form a white-pitted, coarsely **laminated** and crumbly rot (Fig. 69).

The **sporophores** are annual, thin, **resupinate** and white (Fig. 70), forming mostly on slash.

Poria subacida (Peck) Sacc.

Poria subacida attacks a wide range of coniferous and deciduous **hosts** but is most damaging on the true firs, spruce and hemlock.

The early stage of decay appears as a light brown stain. Later, small white pits develop and coalesce to form a mass of white, spongy fibres (Fig. 71) containing small, black flecks. The annual rings may separate to form a **laminate** decay. In the final stage the wood may be completely destroyed, leaving a hollow butt.

The **sporophores** are perennial, **resupinate** and leathery to crust-like (Fig. 72). The lower surface is cream to light yellow and **poroid**; the pores are regular in outline. Sporophores may form on living trees but are generally found on the undersurface of decayed logs or on slash.

Fig. 67. Pocket rot in western red cedar caused by *Polyporus sericeomollis (Poria asiatica).*

Fig. 68. Thin white sporophores of *Polyporus sericeomollis (Poria asiatica).*

65

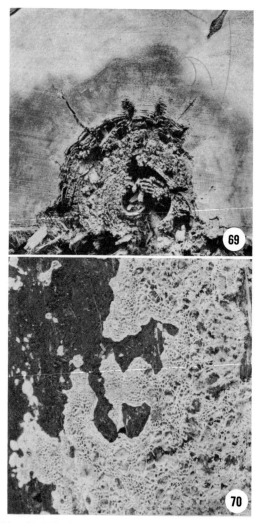

Fig. 69. White-pitted, laminate butt rot of western red cedar caused by *Poria rivulosa (Poria albipellucida)*.

Fig. 70. Annual thin white sporophore of *Poria rivulosa (Poria albipellucida)*.

Fig. 71. White spongy rot in western hemlock caused by *Poria subacida*.

Fig. 72. Perennial, crust-like cream-colored sporophore of *Poria subacida*.

Columnocystis abietina (Pers. ex Fr.) Pouzar
(Stereum abietinum (Pers. ex Fr.) Fr.)
causing brown cubical pocket rot

Columnocystis abietina was once considered to be only a slash destroyer but it is now recognized as a commonly occurring trunk rot in coniferous trees, mainly western hemlock and the true firs. The **fungus** is apparently capable of continued development in unseasoned timber.

The early stage of decay is characterized by a wet, dark brown or black stain that occurs in streaks or patches. The advanced stage develops in pockets (Fig. 73) surrounded by what appears to be sound wood. In the final stage the individual pockets coalesce, forming a more or less continuous column of decay. The decay is soft and friable and is often associated with dark stain, thin cobweb-like accumulations of **mycelium** (Fig. 74) and a characteristic odor resembling that of stored apples.

The **sporophores** are small and shelf-like (Fig. 75), with a roughened, gray to light brown lower surface and a dark brown to nearly black upper surface. The **context** is brown. Sporophores may form on the scarred portions of living trees but more frequently are found on old logs and dead material on the ground.

Ganoderma applanatum (Pers. ex Wallr.) Pat.
(Fomes applanatus (Pers. ex Wallr.) Gill.)
causing white mottled rot

Ganoderma applanatum attacks a wide range of coniferous and deciduous **hosts**. It causes an important decay of dead trees but may gain entrance to living trees through wounds and cause extensive damage.

In the early stage of decay, the affected wood of most species becomes bleached and is encircled by a dark brown stain. In western hemlock, this stage is violet to lilac in color. In the advanced stage, the wood becomes white, mottled and spongy. Black **zone lines** may or may not be present (Fig. 77).

The **sporophores** are perennial, leathery to woody and tend to be flat or plate-like (Fig. 76). The upper surface is light brown to gray and deeply zoned. The margin, when fresh, may be white. The **context** is light brown but may possess a light gray zone. The lower surface is white, turning brown in old specimens or when bruised or marked, hence the common names the "picture fungus" or "artist's conk".

68

Fig. 73. Brown cubical pocket rot in amabilis fir caused by *Columnocystis (Stereum) abietina.*

Fig. 74. Brown cubical rot caused by *Columnocystis (Stereum) abietina* illustrating thin, cobweb-like mycelium (center of photo).

Fig. 75. Dark brown, shelf-like sporophores of *Columnocystis (Stereum)*
abietina.

Fig. 76. Plate-like sporophore of *Ganoderma applanatum*.

Fig. 77. White mottled decay with black zone lines (left hand edge of photo) caused by *Ganoderma applanatum*.

Fomes officinalis (Vill. ex Fr.) Neum.

(*Fomes laricis* Jacq. ex Murr.)

causing brown trunk rot

Fomes officinalis, the quinine **fungus**, attacks a wide range of coniferous **hosts** and may cause severe damage to individual trees. Western larch is the only species known to be attacked extensively, but Sitka spruce and Douglas-fir are also hosts in British Columbia.

The early stage of decay appears as a light yellow to red-brown stain or, in the case of Douglas-fir, as a purple discoloration. The stain may extend for a considerable distance beyond the advanced decay. In the late stage the wood breaks into brown cubes, and thick, white **mycelial** felts (Fig. 78) may form in the shrinkage cracks.

The **sporophores** are relatively large, perennial and vary from hoof-shaped (Fig. 79) to long, pendulous structures. The upper surface is zoned (Fig. 80), white when fresh, but drying to dark gray or light brown in old specimens; a chalky coating, which rubs off as a white powder, may be present. The lower surface is white when fresh, drying to light brown, and is **poroid**; the pores are relatively small and uniform in outline. The **context** is white or gray, relatively soft in texture and is distinctly bitter in taste. Sporophores are formed relatively frequently only on larch, but on all tree species a single sporophore indicates that most of the wood volume has been destroyed.

Fig. 78. Brown trunk rot of Douglas-fir caused by *Fomes officinalis* illustrating the thick, white mycelial felts which form in the shrinkage cracks.

Fig. 79. Perennial, hoof-shaped sporophore of *Fomes officinalis*.

Fig. 80. Zoned upper surface of a *Fomes officinalis* sporophore.

73

Hericium abietis (Weir ex Hubert) K. Harrison

causing long-pitted rot

Hericium abietis is responsible for a frequently occurring butt and trunk rot of western hemlock and the true firs and is known to attack Sitka spruce.

The early stage of decay appears as a yellow to brown heartwood stain. Later, elongated pits, about one-half inch long, are formed and these may contain yellow to white **mycelium.** The rot is similar to red ring rot (Fig. 60) but with *H. abietis* the pits are usually longer and have blunt ends and the general outline of the decay in cross-section tends to be irregular (Fig. 81).

The **sporophores,** annual, soft, fleshy and white, are characterized by a large number of downward-directed spines, approximately one-half to three-quarters of an inch long when fully developed, produced on a much-branched fleshy stalk (Fig. 82). The sporophores are generally found on slash and on the ends of cut logs, but they may also form on wounds on living trees. Because of their fleshy nature they are short-lived.

Fomes robustus Karst.

causing white trunk rot

Fomes robustus causes a white trunk rot of western hemlock, amabilis fir, alpine fir and Douglas-fir. The decay sometimes occurs as a sector of infected wood extending in from the sapwood (Fig. 83). The rot is often found in association with wounds or dead branches and with mistletoe infections which have killed part of the **cambium.**

The early stage of decay appears as a brown to purple stain which may be of irregular shape. In the late stage, the wood has a bleached appearance with occasional light brown areas or streaks. **Zone lines** are usually numerous in the decayed wood.

The **sporophores** are perennial and vary from hoof-shaped, when formed on the main bole (Fig. 84), to **resupinate,** when formed on the lower surface of branches (Fig. 85). The upper surface is dark brown to black and the lower surface is brown and **poroid;** the pores are small and regular in outline.

Fig. 81. Long-pitted rot, pits filled with white mycelium, of western hemlock caused by *Hericium abietis*.

Fig. 82. Fleshy white sporophore of *Hericium abietis* illustrating downward-directed spines.

Fig. 83. Purple-brown incipient decay (upper left) and light brown advanced decay in western hemlock caused by *Fomes robustus*.

Fig. 84. Perennial hoof-shaped sporophores of *Fomes robustus*.
Fig. 85. Resupinate sporophore of *Fomes robustus*.

Polyporus delectans Peck

causing brown stringy trunk rot

Polyporus delectans causes an important trunk rot of black cottonwood.

Decay first becomes apparent as buff to light brown streaks in the heartwood. In the advanced stage of decay the wood becomes light in weight, uniformly dark brown, usually stringy but sometimes **laminate**. Initially, the decay will form pockets of various sizes but in time these usually coalesce to form a column.

The **sporophores** are annual, fleshy to leathery, and of various shapes but usually shelved. The upper and lower surfaces and **context** are white when fresh, drying to light brown (Fig. 86). The lower surface is **poroid**; the pores are small and regular in outline.

Pholiota destruens (Brond.) Gill.

causing yellow laminated butt rot

Pholiota destruens causes one of the most important butt rots of black cottonwood.

In the early stage the decay appears as buff to dark brown streaks in the heartwood. Later, white patches appear giving the wood a faint white-mottled appearance. In the final stage the wood becomes uniformly yellow to tan in color and **laminate** in texture.

The **sporophores** are relatively large mushrooms, often occurring in clusters, which develop on living trees or on slash. When fresh the cap is light brown and covered with white scales (Fig. 87). The gills are white, drying to dark brown. The stem, when present, is white to light brown and is covered with white scales; a white **annulus** is present. The sporophores are abundant from midsummer to late autumn.

Fig. 86. Fleshy white sporophore of *Polyporus delectans*.

Fig. 87. Mushroom fruit bodies of *Pholiota destruens* illustrating white scales on the cap.

Fomes igniarius (L. ex Fr.) Kickx

causing white trunk rot

Fomes igniarius causes an important white trunk rot of aspen.

The early stage of decay appears as a yellow-white stain in the heartwood, usually surrounded by a yellow-green to brown zone. In the advanced stage the soft yellow-white wood usually contains fine black **zone lines** (Fig. 88).

The **sporophores** are perennial, hard, woody, and generally hoof-shaped (Fig. 89). The upper surface is deeply zoned, gray-black to black, and roughened when old. The lower surface is brown and **poroid**; the pores are small and regular in outline. The **context** is rust-brown, often interspersed with silver-gray flecks. Sporophores form on standing trees and on slash; the presence of a single sporophore generally indicates a considerable volume of decay.

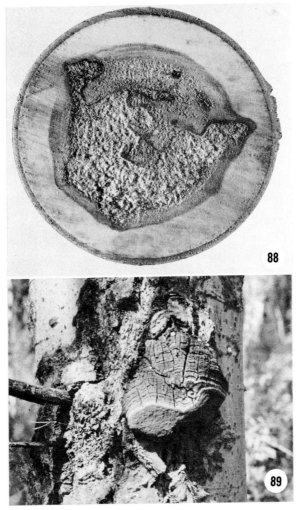

Fig. 88. Yellow-white stringy advanced decay with included black zone lines caused by *Fomes igniarius* in aspen.

Fig. 89. Hoof-shaped sporophores of *Fomes igniarius* illustrating deeply zoned gray-black upper surface.

Fomes fomentarius (L. ex Fr.) Kickx

causing white spongy trunk rot

Fomes fomentarius attacks a number of deciduous species but is most common on birch. It causes decay chiefly in dead timber but can also attack living trees.

Decay first appears as a slight brown discoloration, the wood remaining quite firm. Wood with advanced decay is yellow-white, soft and spongy, and frequently contains brown to black **zone lines** (Fig. 90). Small radial cracks filled with yellow **mycelium** may develop, giving the decay a mottled appearance.

The **sporophores** are perennial, woody or leathery, and usually hoof-shaped (Fig. 91). The upper surface is zoned, gray to brown or gray to black in color, smooth and with a thick crust. The lower surface is brown and **poroid**; the pores are small and regular in outline. The **context** is brown. Sporophores form on standing trees and on slash.

Fig. 90. Yellow-white spongy decay with included black zone lines caused by *Fomes fomentarius* in birch.

Fig. 91. *Fomes fomentarius* sporophore illustrating smooth gray upper surface.

83

Stem Diseases – Sap Rots

Fomes pinicola (Sw. ex Fr.) Cooke

causing brown crumbly rot

Fomes pinicola, the red belt **fungus**, is one of the most frequently occurring decay-producing fungi in British Columbia, attacking a wide range of coniferous and deciduous tree species. It is very common on dead trees and has been termed the scavenger fungus because of its importance in reducing wood to forest litter. It occurs frequently as a sap rot (Fig. 92) but can also gain entrance through wounds and cause considerable damage to the heartwood of living trees (Fig. 93).

The **incipient** stage of decay appears as a light brown stain. Later, the wood breaks into small cubes which are soft and crumbly in texture (Fig. 93). Relatively thick white felts of **mycelium** may form in the shrinkage cracks.

Sporophores are usually found on dead wood but they occasionally develop on living trees in association with wounds. They are perennial, leathery to woody in texture, and hoof-shaped or shelved (Fig. 94). The upper surface (Fig. 95) is usually zoned and ranges in color from dark brown to black. The margin is rounded and often red-brown and lighter than other portions of the upper surface (Fig. 95), hence the common name "red belt fungus". The lower surface is white to cream and **poroid**; the pores are small and regular in outline. The **context** is cream to light brown.

Polyporus volvatus Peck

causing gray sap rot

Polyporus volvatus attacks a wide range of coniferous **hosts** and is extremely common in fire-killed Douglas-fir.

The **fungus** causes a cream to light gray discoloration in the outer sapwood; the discoloration is particularly evident in a radial or tangential section. The affected wood becomes soft and brash.

The **sporophores** are annual, leathery, pouch-like structures (Figs. 96, 97). The upper surface is white to light brown and smooth in texture. The brown **poroid** lower surface is at first completely covered by a hard membrane continuous with the upper surface, hence the common name "pouch fungus" (Fig. 97). Later an opening forms at the base of the membrane (Fig. 98) to permit the release of the **spores**.

Fig. 92. Brown crumbly sap rot in western hemlock caused by *Fomes pinicola*.

Fig. 93. Brown crumbly heart rot in Douglas-fir caused by *Fomes pinicola*.

Fig. 94. Shelf-like sporophore of *Fomes pinicola*.

Fig. 95. Smooth dark brown upper surface of *Fomes pinicola* sporophore showing light red-brown margin.

Fig. 96. Pouch-like sporophore of *Polyporus volvatus*.

Fig. 97. Cross-section through a *Polyporus volvatus* sporophore illustrating membrane completely covering spore surface.

Fig. 98. Sporophore of *Polyporus volvatus* showing hole in membrane that permits the release of the spores.

Lenzites saepiaria (Wulf. ex Fr.) Fr.

causing brown cubical sap rot

Lenzites saepiaria attacks most coniferous and many deciduous species and is commonly associated with deterioration of fire-killed trees and of slash.

The decay first appears as a yellow to yellow-brown discoloration in the sapwood or outer heartwood. The advanced decay is a typical brown cubical rot.

The **sporophores** are small, annual, leathery shelf-like structures (Fig. 99). The upper surface is light to dark cinnamon brown, zoned and roughened. The lower surface is light brown and consists of tough, radiating membranes or gill-like structures (Fig. 100). The **context** is brown.

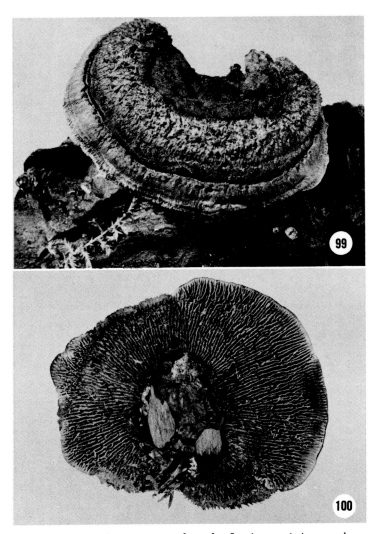

Fig. 99. Cinnamon-brown upper surface of a *Lenzites saepiaria* sporophore.
Fig. 100. Lower surface of a *Lenzites saepiaria* sporophore showing radiating gill-like structures.

89

Hirschioporus abietinus (Dicks. ex Fr.) Donk

(*Polyporus abietinus* Dicks. ex Fr.)

causing pitted sap rot

Hirschioporus abietinus attacks a wide range of coniferous **hosts**. It is of primary importance as a deteriorating agent but is also capable of causing sap rot and heart rot in living trees. It has been reported to have attacked unseasoned wood in service.

In the early stage of decay, the wood becomes yellow and soft. In the advanced stage, small pits develop, elongated in the direction of the grain, which may be filled with a white fibrous material at first but later become empty.

Sporophores rarely form on living trees but may be produced in great abundance on dead trees (Fig. 101) and forest litter. They are relatively small, annual, thin, **effused-reflexed** (Fig. 102) or shelf-like, forming abundantly in bark crevices or on decorticated wood. The upper surface is zoned, light gray and somewhat hairy in texture. The lower surface is purple when fresh, hence the common name "purple conk". The lower surface turns light brown with age.

Other sap rots

A number of other **fungi** cause sap rot and the deterioration of dead wood. Some of the more commonly occurring of these and their most frequently attacked **hosts** are:

Fomes cajanderi Karst. (*Fomes subroseus* (Weir) Overh.) on Douglas-fir.

Peniophora gigantea (Fr.) Massee on Douglas-fir and yellow pine.

Polyporus adustus Willd. ex Fr. on black cottonwood.

Polyporus anceps Peck on Douglas-fir and yellow pine.

Polyporus hirsutus Wulf. ex Fr. on hardwoods.

Polyporus versicolor L. ex Fr. on hardwoods.

Chondrostereum (Stereum) purpureum (Pers. ex Fr.) Pouzar on hardwoods.

Fig. 101. *Hirschioporus (Polyporus) abietinus* sporophores on dead amabilis fir.

Fig. 102. Purple lower surface of thin, effused-reflexed sporophore of *Hirschioporus (Polyporus) abietinus*.

91

Stem and Branch Diseases — Miscellaneous

Burls and galls

Burls are abnormal swellings of the main stem or branches and are among the most conspicuous of the stem diseases. They vary considerably in size, reaching 3 feet or more in diameter in some cases (Fig. 103) but rarely occur in sufficient abundance to warrant concern. Burls result from the abnormal development in number or size of wood cells following disturbance to the **cambial** layer, the cause of which in most cases remains unknown. Dwarf mistletoes cause burls in several coniferous species (Fig. 34).

Galls are localized trunk or branch swellings in which bark tissues are mainly affected with little or no damage to the underlying wood. Small galls, approximately one-half to 1 inch in diameter, are relatively frequent on Douglas-fir and western hemlock; those on Douglas-fir have been attributed to a bacterial agent but in western hemlock (Fig. 104) the cause is still unknown.

Cork-bark

An unusual condition of bark-ridging, referred to as cork-bark and caused by *Dermea rhytidiformans* Funk and Kuijt, is sometimes encountered in alpine fir. Restricted areas of the main stem, seldom exceeding 3 feet in length, are affected (Fig. 105). The condition is characterized by a very thick and deeply furrowed bark, contrasting sharply with normal, relatively smooth bark. Studies have shown that wood quality is adversely affected.

Witches' brooms

Witches' brooms occur on a number of tree species. Mistletoe (Fig. 35), rusts (Fig. 42) and needle diseases (Fig. 112) cause brooming; other brooms of unknown cause occur, sometimes very large and involving much of the tree crown (Fig. 106). False or stimulation brooms may be produced in a number of coniferous species in partially logged areas or on exposed ridges; in these cases the abnormal growth may result from the sudden exposure to light or damage by wind.

Fig. 103. Large burl on the main stem of Engelmann spruce.

Fig. 104. Galls on western hemlock, cause unknown.

Fig. 105. Cork-bark on the stem of alpine fir.

94

Fig. 106. Large stimulation broom in the crown of Douglas-fir, cause unknown.

Needle Blights and Casts of Coniferous Trees

Rhabdocline pseudotsugae Syd.

Rhabdocline weirii Parker & Reid

causing Douglas-fir needle blight

Rhabdocline pseudotsugae is responsible for a needle blight of Douglas-fir and is confined to this **host.** Infected needles are prematurely cast, thus depriving the tree of part of its photosynthetic capacity and reducing tree growth and vigor. Severely attacked trees usually have **chlorotic** foliage (Fig. 107) and very thin and open crowns, reducing their suitability for Christmas trees. This disease occurs in both coastal and interior regions of the province but is less severe in the coastal forms of Douglas-fir. Occasional trees show marked resistance to the disease. **Epidemic** infection years appear to occur in cycles and to depend on climatic conditions during the infection period.

Infection takes place in the new foliage in the spring. In the fall, yellow spots that later turn red-brown appear (Figs. 108, 109). **Fruiting bodies** do not develop until spring, at least 1 year after infection. The fruiting bodies are small, orange-brown, raised pustules, generally occurring on the lower side but occasionally on the upper side of the needle. The infected needle drops shortly after **spores** are released.

Rhabdocline pseudotsugae has been divided into two species *R. pseudotsugae* which includes subspecies *pseudotsugae* and *epiphylla,* and *R. weirii* which includes subspecies *weirii, oblonga* and *obovata.*

Fig. 107. Red-brown chlorotic foliage of Douglas-fir infected by *Rhabdocline pseudotsugae*.

Fig. 108. Yellow spots in a Douglas-fir needle indicative of Rhabdocline infection.

Fig. 109. Next stage after the yellow spots in the Rhabdocline infection of Douglas-fir needles.

Didymascella thujina (Durand) Maire (*Keithia thujina* Durand)

causing leaf blight of western red cedar

Didymascella thujina may cause extensive damage to western red cedar foliage but seldom concurrently throughout the entire crown. It has been reported as a cause of mortality in seedlings but it causes only a reduction in growth and vigor in older trees. The **fruiting bodies** appear as small, dark brown eruptions on the foliage scales (Fig. 110). At a later stage the fruiting bodies drop out, leaving characteristic cavities in the dead, gray foliage. Severely affected trees have a scorched appearance, at first red, later turning gray.

Herpotrichia juniperi (Duby) Petr. (*Herpotrichia nigra* Hartig)

causing brown felt blight

Herpotrichia juniperi attacks a wide range of coniferous **hosts** but is most common on the true firs and spruce, generally occurring at high elevations. The **fungus** develops on foliage under the snow. The affected foliage is covered with a dense, dark brown mat of **mycelium** (Fig. 111), hence the name "brown felt blight". Small trees may be killed following repeated attack. The **fruiting bodies** consist of small, black, globular bodies that appear in the mycelial felt.

Fig. 110. Leaf blight of western red cedar caused by *Didymascella (Keithia) thujina.*

Fig. 111. Brown felt blight on alpine fir caused by *Herpotrichia juniperi.*

99

Elytroderma deformans (Weir) Darker

causing elytroderma needle cast

Elytroderma needle cast is the most important needle disease of yellow pine and lodgepole pine in British Columbia. Infection takes place in the late summer but evident **symptoms** do not appear until early spring of the following year. Groups of needles may turn red and die, forming conspicuous **flags**. The **fungus** becomes perennial in the twigs, often stimulating them to form relatively small, open and tufted witches' brooms (Fig. 112). The **fruiting bodies** develop as small dark streaks on the dead foliage (Fig. 113). The growth rate of the tree may be seriously affected. Heavily attacked, severely suppressed or otherwise weakened trees may be killed.

Fig. 112. Small tufted witches' brooms on yellow pine caused by twig infection by *Elytroderma deformans*.

Fig. 113. *Elytroderma deformans* fruiting on yellow pine needles.

101

Hypodermella laricis Tub.

causing larch needle blight

Larch needle blight is a common and sometimes spectacular disease of western larch. Needle infection takes place in the spring. **Symptoms** first show in early summer with a sudden and drastic change in foliage color to reddish brown. The **fruiting bodies** appear as small black spots or streaks on the needles. Tufts of infected dead foliage persist at least 1 year after the healthy foliage has been shed. Seedlings and spur shoots on young trees may be killed but the major influence of larch needle blight is on tree growth.

Other needle blights and casts occurring commonly on coniferous trees in British Columbia include the following:

Scirrhia pini Funk and Parker (*Dothistroma pini* Hulbary) causes a needle blight of most 2- and 3-needle pines. It can be recognized by a brick-red banding of the needles (Fig. 114).

Lophodermella concolor (Dearn.) Darker on lodgepole pine.

Davisomycella (Hypodermella) ampla (Davis) Darker on lodgepole pine.

Lirula (Hypodermella) abietis-concoloris (Mayr ex Dearn.) Darker on *Abies* spp.

Lirula (Lophodermium) macrospora (Hartig) Darker causes a needle blight particularly on Sitka spruce. The disease is easily recognized by the black lines on the needles which remain on the twigs after they have been killed (Fig. 115).

Delphinella abietis (Rostr.) E. Muell. on alpine fir. The young fir shoots are killed soon after they appear, but **spores** are not produced on the needles until the following spring.

Lophodermium pinastri (Schrad. ex Hook.) Chev. on Scots pine (*Pinus sylvestris* L.) Christmas tree stock.

Fig. 114. *Scirrhia (Dothistroma) pini* fruiting on *Pinus pinaster* needles.

Fig. 115. *Lirula (Lophodermium) macrospora* fruiting on Sitka spruce needles.

Needle and Cone Rusts of Coniferous Trees

Coniferous trees are attacked by a number of different foliage rusts. These diseases are capable of killing seedlings and very small trees and of reducing the growth and vigor of mature trees. The most conspicuous **spore** state on the primary **hosts** appears as small, yellow or occasionally white, pustules or horns (Fig. 116) on the surface of the needles. Severely infected trees may appear uniformly yellow.

Some typical foliage rusts are:

Melampsora medusae Thuem. on current year's needles of Douglas-fir; damage, except to seedlings, has been slight. Severity of the rust depends on the climate and on the presence of aspen, the alternate host, in the vicinity.

Chrysomyxa ledicola Lagerh. may cause heavy defoliation of spruce but only in and near swamps or bogs where the alternate host, Labrador tea (*Ledum groenlandicum* Oeder), is plentiful.

Pucciniastrum epilobii Otth causes yellow needle rust of the current year's needles of *Abies*. This rust is most damaging to alpine fir in logged and burned areas where the alternate host, fireweed (*Epilobium angustifolium* L.), abounds.

There are two cone rusts of importance in British Columbia, *Chrysomyxa monesis* Ziller, alternating between Sitka spruce and single delight (*Moneses uniflora* (L.) Gray), and *Chrysomyxa pirolata* Wint., (Fig. 117) alternating between spruce and wintergreen (*Pyrola* spp.). Yellow, powdery masses of spores appear on the surface of the cone scales, indicating substantial internal development of the **fungus** within the cone and the destruction of seed. In **epidemic** years, *Chrysomyxa pirolata* may cause severe damage over extensive areas in the interior region of the province.

Fig. 116. Aecial horns of *Milesina laeviuscula* (Diet) Hirat. f. rust on *Abies grandis* needles.

Fig. 117. Rust infection of black spruce cones. The cone on the right is healthy. The infected cone on the left illustrates the yellow powdery spore masses produced by *Chrysomyxa pirolata*.

105

Foliage Diseases of Broadleaved Trees

Foliage diseases occur commonly on deciduous tree species. With the exception of the rusts, they are caused by **fungi** generally capable of development within both dead and living tissues; they require only one **host** to complete their life cycle. The **fruiting bodies** appear as blisters or as small black dots about the size of a pin head (Figs. 118, 119), sometimes clustered in groups, depending upon the specific fungus responsible for the attack.

Typical examples include:

Melampsora medusae Thuem., causing leaf rust of aspen; alternate host is Douglas-fir.

Venturia macularis (Fr.) E. Muell. & von Arx causing leaf and shoot blight of aspen.

Marssonina brunnea (Ell. & Ev.) Sacc., causing brown leaf spot of aspen.

Ciborinia whetzelii (Seav.) Seav., causing ink spot of aspen.

Uncinula salicis (DC. ex Mérat) Wint., causing powdery mildew of aspen and cottonwood.

Melampsora occidentalis Jacks., causing a leaf rust of cottonwood; alternate host is Douglas-fir.

Venturia populina (Vuill.) Fabric., causing leaf and shoot blight of cottonwood.

Drepanopeziza populorum (Desm.) Hoehn., causing brown leaf spot of cottonwood and aspen.

Linospora tetraspora G. E. Thomps., causing leaf spot of cottonwood.

Taphrina populi-salicis Mix, causing leaf blister of cottonwood.

Melampsoridium betulinum (Fr.) Kleb., causing leaf rust of birch.

Rhytisma punctatum (Pers.) Fr. causing black leaf spot of broadleaf maple (Figs. 118, 119).

Melampsora epitea Thuem., causing a leaf rust of all species of willow.

Rhytisma salicinum (Pers.) Fr., causing tar spot of willow.

Coccomyces quadratus (Schum. & Kunze) Karst., causing tar spot on foliage of arbutus.

Didymosporium arbuticola Zeller, causes brown leaf spot with purplish to reddish margins of arbutus.

Fig. 118. Black leaf spot on broadleaf maple caused by *Rhytisma punctatum*.

Fig. 119. Close-up of spots shown in Fig. 118.

GLOSSARY

Acute. Pointed, sharp-edged; not prolonged.

Annulus. The ring of tissue left on the stalk of a mushroom when the partial veil breaks.

Callus. Wound tissue, composed of soft parenchymatous tissue formed on or about injured surfaces of stems and roots.

Cambium. A layer of generative cells which gives rise to secondary wood (xylem) and secondary inner bark (phloem).

Canker. A disease of woody plants characterized by sharply delimited necrosis of the cortical tissues and malformation of the bark caused by recurring killing back of the **cambium** layer.

Chlorosis, chlorotic. An unseasonable yellowing of the foliage, symptomatic of a chlorophyll deficiency in the leaf tissues.

Conk. A **fruit body** of a wood-destroying **fungus**.

Context. The inner or body tissue of a **fruit body** which supports the fruiting surface.

Dieback. The progressive dying, from the tip downward, of twigs, branches, tops or roots.

Effused-reflexed. Spread out over the substratum and turned back at the margin.

Epidemic. A widespread high level of disease incidence beyond normal proportions.

Flag, flagging. A dying, or recently dead, twig or branch, the foliage of which contrasts in color with the normal green foliage of living trees.

Fruit body, fruiting body (sporophore, conk). In the higher **fungi**, a structure that bears the spore-producing structures and **spores**.

Fungus, fungi. One group of the lower plants that lack chlorophyll, thus requiring a **host** from which to obtain food.

Fusiform. Spindle shaped, tapering at both ends.

Host. A plant or other organism that furnishes subsistence to, or harbors, a **parasite**.

Hypha, hyphae. A **fungus** filament.

Infection court. The place on or in the **host** where the incubation activity of the **pathogen** takes place; the immediate neighborhood of a point of infection.

Incipient. An early stage in decay in which the wood may show discoloration but is not otherwise visibly altered.

Inoculum. **Spores** or tissue of a **pathogen** that serve to initiate disease in a plant.

Laminate. Separated into sheets or layers.

Lesion. A definite, localized area of dead tissue, a circumscribed diseased area.

Mycelium. Collective term for **hyphae** or **fungus** filaments.

Obligate parasite. A **parasite** that is incapable of existing independently of living tissues.

Parasite. An organism that draws a part or the whole of its nourishment from another living organism.

Pathogen. An organism capable of causing disease.

Poroid. The fruiting surface of a **fruit body** having more or less evident pores.

Resinosis. An abnormal exudation of resin or pitch from conifers.

Resupinate. A **fruit body** reclined or flat on the substratum.

Rhizomorph. Strand or cord of compact **mycelium**, often dark colored.

Sign. Expression of the causal agent of a disease.

Spore. The reproductive structure in **fungi** and other cryptograms, corresponding to a seed in flowering plants.

Sporophore. See **fruit body**.

Stipitate. Possessing a stem or stalk.

Symptom. Expression of the **host** indicating the presence of disease.

Virulence. Degree of pathogenicity.

Zone lines. Narrow, dark-brown or black lines in decayed wood, generally caused by **fungi.**

HOST INDEX OF INFECTIOUS DISEASES

112

1245-4-74-6M